Price Guide

SENSATIONAL '60s

DOLL ALBUM
by A. Glenn Mandeville

Published by

Hobby House Press

Hobby House Press, Inc.
Grantsville, Maryland 21536

DEDICATION

The 1960s belongs to all of us who were lucky enough to be young, aware enough to be hip, and steady enough to make it through a fascinating, kaleidoscope of a decade. To my generation who made the '60s the most wonderful decade ever, I dedicate this book. We are widely imitated, but seldom duplicated.

CREDITS

Some very special people helped make this project possible. To the late Diane Serico, thanks for your love of dolls from the '60s. To the late Bob Gantz, thank you for your photographic assistance. Technical assistance by Dick Tahsin, Linda Collie, and Judy Traina. Finally I would like to thank my mother and father...I don't know how you ever survived the decade!

All dolls shown are either from the author's collection, or courtesy of Mandeville's Antiques and Collectibles unless otherwise noted.

The word mark BARBIE, the Barbie doll and character likenesses, the color "Barbie pink" and associated trademarks are owned by Mattel, Inc. ©1996 Mattel, Inc. All Rights Reserved. Mattel makes no representation as to the authenticity of the materials contained herein. All opinions are those of the author and not of Mattel.

Sensational '60s is an independent study by the author A. Glenn Mandeville and published by Hobby House Press, Inc. The research and publication of this book was not sponsored in any way by the manufacturers of the dolls, the doll costumes, and the doll accessories featured in this study. Photographs of the collectibles were from dolls, costumes, or accessories belonging to A. Glenn Mandeville at the time the picture was taken unless otherwise credited with the caption.

The information as to the ownership pertains to documentary materials contemporary with the doll or doll's accessories. Ownership of the registered trademark, the trademark, or the copyright may have expired or been transferred to another owner.

In order to capture the greatest detail of the dolls and accessories in the photographic process, the dolls and accessories will appear a different size than in real life.

The values given within this book are intended as value guides rather than arbitrarily set prices. The values quoted are as accurate as possible but in the case of errors, typographical, clerical, or otherwise, the author and publisher assume no liability nor responsibility for any loss incurred by users of this book.

Front Cover: A 1966 *American Girl BARBIE*® doll in a Sears mink wrap.
Title Page: Glamour Misty is ready to meet the Beatles in this sweatshirt that was a pak accessory for Tammy and Glamour Misty. The Beatles are not named on the shirt, but there is no question it is them. "Ya Ya Ya" was a lyric from their song, "She Loves You".
Back Cover: The ultimate *Tammy* is this platinum blonde doll with a rooted braid on the top of her head, wearing the ultimate Tammy outfit, *America's Sweetheart*. Tammy had that innocence that America worshipped in the early 1960s.

Additional copies of this book may be purchased at $29.95 (plus postage and handling) from

Hobby House Press, Inc.
1 Corporate Drive
Grantsville, Maryland 21536
1-800-554-1447
or from your favorite bookstore or dealer.

©1996 A. Glenn Mandeville

ISBN: 0-87588-469-5

TABLE OF CONTENTS

The Toy Boom

Early '60s Dolls

Mid '60s Dolls

Late '60s Dolls

PART I
The Sensational '60s...A Decade in Review

To the young of today, it is the standard by which they resentfully must compete. For the baby boomers, it was the decade of their lives. To those who were then over 50, it was a mystery and a time too frequently in turmoil. For many, it was the best time ever. A decade of new designs and creative attitudes. It was the sensational '60s.

Never before in world history had so much change happened so quickly. Originality flourished. Fresh new ideas were the norm instead of imitations and recreations of the past so often seen today. Traditions lost, brave new worlds explored, drugs, sex, and rock and roll all dominated a decade that few will ever forget. It was the '60s.

Like any other decade, the beginning years were a carry over from the 1950s. The social graces, the class distinctions, white gloves on Sunday and the other trappings of fashion, were all prominent requirements of refinement in the early '60s. It was still the Eisenhower years in America. One had pride and a belief in truth, justice, and the American way, rich or poor.

Illustration 1. The glamour of the late '50 as seen in the movie *Imitation of Life* with Lana Turner and John Gavin would be replaced with a youth rebellion by the end of the decade. *Movie Star News* photo.

Illustration 2. Sandra Dee would be the representative of an entire generation that was always in love with being a teenger in love. *Movie Star News* photo.

Like a real live television sitcom, millions of American families actually lived the life portrayed on "The Donna Reed Show", and "Leave it to Beaver". Respect and reverence, mixed with pride and caring — it was the American way that had worked since the end of World War II.

Across America, Dad worked, and Mom was there after school with cookies and praises for golden stars on schoolwork. The weekends were filled with pursuing the good life. Mowing the lawn, cooking on the grill, playing catch in the backyard and going to church made Sunday a special day. It was a nation that seemed at peace with itself after decades of The Great Depression and two World Wars.

To many outside the large middle and upper classes that made up the bulk of America, things were a bit rougher, but the respect that one had for oneself, one's family, and the community at large were still in tact, even in the poorest of neighborhoods. Class and money were not the same thing in the late '50s and early '60s.

Respect for family and traditions did not have a price tag on it. A woman wore a nice dress and a hat with a veil to church on Sunday whether she was the downstairs maid or the owner of the house. It was about always being a gentleman and a lady and acting like a public relations firm for your family. Dignity and class were everyones for the asking, regardless of socioeconomic position. Bars of soap and cans of paint could cross any financial barrier.

It was a world that would quickly come to an end and be replaced with a "do your own thing" mentality by the end of the decade. Change was about to happen, and things would never be the same again.

Like a carousel ride, the dance would spin round and round, bringing a new wave of people to the forefront and a new way of living into the spotlight.

Change...sometimes for the better, occasionally for the worse, but never stagnant would be the password of the times. It was the decade that forever changed America and so with all change, it was exhilarating, exhausting, and scary. To the young, it was a fun ride they would never forget and for those too old or too unwilling to change, it was a decade that would fearfully forecast the frantic, fast paced way we live today.

In 1960, Princess Margaret Rose announced her engagement to Anthony Armstrong-Jones. Tea was at 4pm sharp. Back in the United States, pop culture was already exploding.

To those of us who grew up in the '50s and '60s, pop culture was something you took for granted. Television was a given, with Lucy, Donna and Dobie...so was a radio with rock and roll blasted by your favorite DJ nightly into your room and even later on your personal headphones.

In the day to day existence, it was only natural that your hairstyle mirrored the latest teen trends, and it was a given that the idol whose records you adored and for whom you would lay down your life would be gone in a couple of years. It was all taken for granted that you were a teen prince or princess in the making just like in the magazines!

Never mind that your room was littered with remnants of your youth. The young teen was still very much a child when it came time for toys. Growing up was scary, and keeping one's foot in the door of childhood kept one secure from the ever quickening demands of being a teenager. BARBIE® dolls and boys could be said in the same breath by many a fourteen year old girl in the early 1960s!

Never before had so many elements come together at the same time for so many. The baby boomers were now restless "almost" teens who knew nothing but the good life. Books, records, clothes, and dances all carried a significance far beyond the casual. They were your LIFE!

In Philadelphia, television dance shows such as "American Bandstand", made local celebrities out of South Philadelphia teens whose asset was that they could dance better than dancers from an MGM musical. The world watched as Philly danced.

Free from cares about money, wars, politics, and problems, the young teen of the early '60s had free time galore. This was not time previous generations spent doing laundry or tilling the field. There were machines for that. Being a young teen meant being hip and in LOVE. In love with Ricky, with Elvis, with Shelley, or Annette...with ANYONE who represented the perfection of what you wanted to be. It was a life your parents did not have and could not understand.

The toys of the decade would reflect this desire of a child to be a perfect replica...or as close as one could come, to that ultimate ideal of teen idol perfection. It was not going to be a decade of coo and wet baby dolls, but of sophisticated teenage dolls who forever would change the destiny of women, as well as forward thinking young boys.

The early '60s saw the introduction of the BARBIE® doll. Actually designed in the mid '50s and introduced in 1959, the shapely teen-age fashion model doll was actually a harsh and garish reminder that the youth of the previous decade were more interested in looking like a younger version of their socialite mothers than in expressing themselves and their own "taste".

In fact the doll was already outdated a year into her career and had to be revamped to fit the image of the teenage girl so increasingly popularized by television and magazines aimed at the preteen and young teen of the early '60s.

Previous generations of children and preteens, emulated adult stars of the day as best they could. "How to be more like Lana Turner, Bette Davis, and Joan Crawford" touted the movie magazines of the day.

"Learn how YOU can look like Norma Shearer" screamed the covers, even if you were twelve years old. The teen girls of the '40s and '50s looked to adults and not to their peers to be their mentors. In the '60s, heros came from within the generation and not from the past. This factor alone made the late '50s and early '60s so different from the decades before.

The new generation of '60s children was in love with only those who "understood" those just like themselves. Through magazines that sported the word "teen" some place in the title, this new breed of preteens wanted their own kind to show them the way to perfection. It was also a scary thing being the idol, as well as the one doing the idolizing. Often neither side could handle the pressure.

Teen magazines shouted "How to do YOUR hair like Shelley Fabares" and "Why Connie Stevens will never cut her ponytail!" These were the beginning battle cries in millions of American homes as children and teenagers began to discover that the decades old traditions forced upon them needed a little MODification. Indeed the word MOD, a euphemism for modern, would be the password of the decade.

To the reader of this epistle whose life was less than the glorification proposed within, the glaring and often unpleasant truth was that you were either pretty, perky, pony tailed, and popular, with a great personality and a wonderful family, or you wanted to be. Case in point, sad but true.

For boys of the early '60s, being the jock was secondary to a head full of pompadour hair, a "pretty" face, and a voice that passed with the reverb on the mike turned up on high. Fluttering lashes and a sexy smile would beat steroid induced biceps anytime. It was a time of fantasy. A Walt Disney dream life come true for the baby boomer child and teenager.

To those outside the loop because of race, looks, location (who could look like they belonged on the set of "Gidget" in North Dakota in January?), the early part of the decade was not so kind. There was an eerie conformity in being a non conformist. What girl didn't want to be Sandra Dee? What boy didn't long to be Ricky Nelson? The question, "Did THEY want

Illustration 3. Ricky Nelson was one of many teen idols of the period. The heroes of this generation came from within instead of the traditional often older celebrities of the past. *Movie Star News* photo.

Illustration 4. By the middle of the decade, a more modern teenager was a popular image. Sally Field did it well as Gidget in a hit television series from the mid '60s. Note the paisley print blouse. *Movie Star News* photo.

to be themselves?", was never asked by adoring fans lost in middle America to whom they offered escape from the ordinary, everyday way of life.

To those of a different race, the comparisons were even more unkind. America was WASP and white in those early '60s. Even Jewish and Italian names were "Americanized". Often off came the "berg" and the "witz". Italian names endings in "a", "i" or "o" were Anglicized also. Just ask Frankie Avalon, Connie Francis, and Bobby Rydell. To pass for being "old money" from Greenwich, Connecticut was the American Dream.

Resentment for not being among the "chosen" was clouded by the acceptance of those who could come the closest to achieving the coveted images of the period. Imitation was the sincerest form of flattery. It was often called "passing", and it applied to most anyone outside the American Dream image who was lucky enough to disguise themselves enough to fit in the accepted mold with a name change and a nose job.

Even the media was kin in those days, because the country WANTED to be happy. If a movie idol was thin because of anorexia, who wanted to listen! Until a troubled life reached the suicidal point, it was not a media circus like today. A celebrity was worshiped from afar, not from a helicopter flying over their swimming pool with a telephoto lens at midnight on Christmas Eve!

Even young love was based on the premise that a kiss was enough, and if you do more and get caught, shame and humiliation will remove you from the early '60s pop culture cycle of beach parties, pizza parlors, and sock hops.

In disgrace, you would quickly become an "adult", with all its self attached burdens; the wonderful world of teendom

Illustration 5. America was still clinging to traditional values as late as 1966 as shown by Lana Turner and John Forsythe in *Madame X*. Just like the characters in the movie, times were changing quickly. *Movie Star News* photo.

would be taken away forever. It was a self policing society of teen idols and their wanna-bes. A perfect symbiotic relationship.

Parents of the early '60s could tolerate this mysterious change of venue they did not understand, because Sandra Dee, Shelly Fabares, and Annette...Ricky Nelson, Fabian, and Frankie Avalon were living the life that had been denied them due to their patriotism and hard work. To a mother whose Sweet Sixteen party in the '30s consisted of a remade hand-me-down dress, shopping for the easy care crinolined party dresses made for a princess, allowed her a second chance on the runway of life.

So far in the decade, "daddy's little girl" and "the chip off the old block" were different, but tolerable. Perhaps the teen puppy love and gyrating rock and roll were a bit over the accepted edge, but it was still within the realm of most families level of tolerance. All that would soon change forever.

Is there anyone who was alive in 1962, that does not know where they were the moment President Kennedy's assassination was announced? For me, it was study hall in 10th grade. The school was the same one my mother had graduated from and my grandfather had served as president of the school board. Life was simple then. Suddenly...in one moment, a moment we still do not know the full truth about...everything changed.

Over the loud speakers came the words, "We are sorry to announce that President Kennedy has been assassinated". The following days of relentless drum beats would make my generation march later to a very different drummer.

Caroline, John-John, and a steadfast Jacqueline ushered out my innocence. More than any childhood trauma, the very thought that our world was in chaos created the tidal wave of change that followed.

Camelot had died, and for many, the social orders were collapsing. Racial issues began to surface. Women were asking why? Sexual minorities were out of the closet. Pop culture began taking off more than ever. The entire generation was restless.

Children of this period would be the last generation to know a quality in toys never to be seen again. They languished over

Illustration 6. Television shows such as "Lost in Space" showed the typical American family, but in atypical situations. *Movie Star News* photo.

the changes in their lives and for many, the rush to grow up meant that toys were being aimed at a younger and younger child...one whose tastes could be easily satisfied with "suggestions" of the real thing, rather than zippers that really zipped, or accessories that actually worked.

Other idols beaconed beyond the toy department. The Twist, The Stomp, The Mashed Potato...Girl Groups and the emerging Motown Sound that would bring black singers into the mainstream of America, all competed with that doll on the toy shelf.

Shirley Temple was replaced with Chubby Checker. Deanna Durbin and Judy Garland were merely holiday references. To be able to do The Twist in the fourth grade was far more a status symbol than being able to cut out a Betsy McCall paper doll with dazzling perfection.

Children were being dragged into teendom earlier and younger. Without the skills to control their behavior, the future was inevitable. The young and the restless were about to collide with established traditions.

When did it happen? I really can't remember the exact date. For years I wanted to look like my well dressed grandfather. Brooks Brothers blue boxes and Macy's red ones competed for closet space in their Victorian home. I couldn't wait for the day when I would get as a gift, a miniature Stetson hat box with a tiny hat that I could redeem for a full size fedora. Why suddenly didn't it matter? Who wanted or cared about an animal logo on their shirt!

The British Invasion. The second one. It made the first one in Colonial times look like nothing. In high school, within weeks, the arrival of the Beatles erased years of ivy covered traditions. The children in elementary school could sing "I want to hold your hand" better than any nursery rhyme. It all happened so fast.

Suddenly I didn't like what my grandfather was wearing. Who wanted to look like they were in their fifties at sixteen? Geez, could I get MY hair to hang straight down in my face like Paul McCartney? Wow! I wanted to be MOD. Quickly the battle lines were drawn.

Illustration 7. Women's roles were changing in the '60s, and Barbara Eden did it with a style few mortals could imagine on the television show "I Dream of Jeannie". *Movie Star News* photo.

Illustration 8. "That Girl" Marlo Thomas lived alone and liked it. Her morals were just as high as her hemlines in a decade of change. *Movie Star News* photo.

For the younger child, this was reflected in the toys of the day. Gone were the demure Sweet Sue and the big sister Revlon doll and her tales of how to grow up to look like mommy. No one wanted to look like mommy unless she was the lead singer of the Sangri-las!

This was the BIG time, this was TODAY! The only people that could tell you how to look young, fresh, and alive were those who WERE young, fresh, and alive.

The dolls of the day reflected this much to the dismay of the blue haired dowager shopping for her granddaughter. BARBIE® doll and her friends now no longer looked like Jacqueline at an Embassy tea, but sported paisley mini skirts that if were any shorter, would just be tee shirts.

The "refined" dolls of the day, Madame Alexander, Effanbee®, and others were desperately trying to connect with the parent who wanted to counter this influence with the traditions of the past...art, literature, heros of fiction...but it was a losing battle. BARBIE® doll and friends like PJ and black friend Christie, were breaking down the walls of the elite in both shocking and positive ways.

Many children no longer dreamed of debutante balls and becoming Shriners. The men's lodges and women's clubs were a mockery to the young and hip. Class among the young no longer meant a thousand dollar beaded dress, a fake French curled hairpiece, and white gloves. Tickets to see the Beatles at Madison Square Gardens and polka dot bell bottoms were the new status symbols.

The natural result of all this was that parents "freaked out" to coin a new phrase of the day. Desperately trying to shed the vestiges of the past, the new child and teenager rebelled even more. Symbols such as hearth and home were meaningless and thus their being taken away held no threat to the newly "liberated" generation. When one didn't desire what was being offered, it could hardly be held up as a prize for good behavior.

All this was not ignored by the toy industry in the mid '60s. What did these children want, aside from just skipping childhood altogether and moving right into the world of the MODern teenager?

Collectively, with Mattel at the helm, the toy industry made their move (I call it "Cosmetic Rebellion Response") and it soon caught on. It was the parents biggest weapon. No grades...no car. Don't clean your room, no Beatles concert, tickets or not. Suddenly the rebellious noticed that without "wheels" and a chauffeur, the best seats in the house were a waste of money. There had to be a compromise.

In my own life, that peace came hard. I had never worked a day in my life, but my parents refused to buy me the striped overalls and poor boy caps I yearned for. So...I got a job and learned the value of a dollar, BUT I bought what I wanted with the money. Records, MOD clothes and my ever favorite, BARBIE® doll! My parents weren't pleased, but I was doing what they said...if you want it, buy it yourself. A truce...shaky, but still in place, existed in the mid to late '60s in many households. It was the same with the doll manufacturers.

Mattel "eased" BARBIE® doll and her family into the MOD scene by making it seem superficial. The dolls' standards were as high as their skirts. It was simply cosmetic and for fashion. No "causes" here, just fun dressing in the latest fashion.

The smart parents of the day caught on fast. Who cared if that Beatle haircut annoyed the heck out of you, if your son was on the Honor Roll. Bell bottoms are fine...just be in by midnight. Compromise. Without it, many children and teens simply left home and became statistics of the lost and unaccounted for. Hippie ghettos like Haight-Ashbury beckoned to those who were unable to work a deal with the family.

The entertainment industry caught on fast to "Cosmetic Rebellion". Both "That Girl" and "I Dream of Jeannie" might have looked like hookers in the '40s, but they were still "good girls" who just liked MOD clothes twenty years later. It was the perfect solution and worked for the rest of the decade, in fact even well into the '70s.

Certainly Laurie Partridge and Marsha Brady had the highest of moral standards...along with the shortest of skirts. It WAS possible to look VERY high fashion, and still be Grace Kelley at heart.

The doll industry was very happy with this new found truce to the '60s dilemma. Dolls were issued of Barbara Eden, and other '60s icons that captured their high fashion appeal, AND their high moral standards. Innocence mixed with the modern pop culture.

Gone for the most part, were the lavish Madame Alexander dolls in ball gowns. The company was trying to remain current by making dolls representing the Von Trapp family in *The Sound of Music* and continuing their focus on literature and fine art. They were successful in maintaining their position by offering "better" dolls to a higher class of clientele at upper class department stores.

A new trend of the later '60s was the "gimmicky" doll. Technology had gone beyond the drink and wet dolly stage; few little girls were interested in changing diapers anyway. The new genre of dolls featured battery operated singing voices and lifelike movement. It was a decade of experimentation unparalleled in today's high stakes toy industry.

When looking back, the one thing of the '60s that stands out, is that everything was really fresh and new. The economy was strong and faith in new products equally so, which meant that a company could take a chance in new territory.

Today, the remakes of '60s and '70s fashions and toys is almost insulting to those who lived through it and had them the first time. The attitude is that if it brought in money once, it can again with a new generation. The economic climate is so explosive today that experimentation leads to instant bankruptcy if the concept fails. Such was not the case in the '60s. Today life spins on a dime. With costs so high, if the returns aren't there in a month, the line is discontinued. BARBIE® doll would not exist today had that been the thinking in 1959.

By the later part of the decade, the "Cosmetic Rebellion" and those who were truly disenchanted may have looked alike, but there the difference stopped. The same girl living in a commune, still a child herself nursing one or more babies and dealing with a new host of diseases, often looked little different from the girl next door and her fringed suede mini skirt that she was only allowed to wear after school and on weekends.

Before the end of the decade, the drug culture and the dropping of the words "pride and respect" from the youthful vocabulary would end the decade on a bad note for many lost in a world far worse than the one they were rebelling against.

As for dolls, the golden age of dolls would be over until the doll artist movement of the early 1990s. Quality would decline in the '70s to the point where even BARBIE® doll herself would be unrecognizable to the original creators, in my opinion.

Parents hassled by time restraints..."free love" turned into divorce and latch key children untrained to take care of their possessions...would cheapen the toy industry.

As the '60s drew to a close, pop culture and the toy manufacturers joined hands to bring child and parent together again. Celebrity dolls and television themed toys would help bridge the gap left by the pop culture invasion. Even military themed toys such as GI Joe®, would pursue an "adventure" theme doing battle with nature and ancient treasures, rather than presenting a conquering hero perception.

The Sensational '60s represents to me a time when children and teenagers were given new opportunities. Restraints such as color, sex, and money, did not matter as much as the decade wore on, as finding an inner strength to set your own value system in a world of constant change and having the will to stick to it.

For toys and dolls, the changes from Camelot to chaos left us with a decade of some of the most unusual and highly collectible objects of this century. BARBIE® and GI Joe® are industry leaders over thirty years later! The Alexander Doll Company is still introducing children to the classics and familiar names like Ginny and Effanbee® are with us once again.

I will always be grateful for being a child and then a teenager in the turbulent, yet always challenging 1960s. It was a time to be young and alive. To me, it was and still is, the most creative and interesting decade in history. There has never been a time like it since. It could be a rising high of new experience, or a mind laden trap for the naive.

MOD, exciting, and all consuming...It was, and still is to us who lived it all...the *Sensational '60s*.

Illustration 9. The forerunner of the teenage fashion doll was the *Revlon Doll* by the Ideal Toy Company of Hollis, NY. Her "big sister" theme was a new concept.

Sensational '60s Dolls

THE TOY BOOM

The end of World War II brought a prosperity previously unknown in this country. Returning veterans were treated like royalty...jobs were plentiful, ladies were waiting, and suburbia beckoned.

Throughout the land, "track" housing sprung up around steel mills, manufacturing facilities and large and small businesses. A job for every GI was the slogan; life settled down for many into a pattern of normalcy. This translated into Mom at home with hopefully a son and a daughter, and Dad working a normal business day to come home to his well cared for house and his darling family. For many, the American Dream was a reality.

The idea of having children for the sake of one's personal enjoyment was a fairly new concept in rural America. Previous generations had balanced the need for extra hands in the field against extra mouths to feed. These new children would be called Baby Boomers, and psychologists would pronounce the years 1946-1964 as the birth years of a generation that would go down in history as the most catered to group of youngsters ever born in recorded history.

The early boom children were indeed very special. They were the reward promised to the lonely GI in a letter read on Christmas Eve during an Air Raid. They were the future to the woman who worked the soup kitchens as a volunteer. These early baby boomer children would be the little prince and princesses of the household.

As the '50s progressed into the '60s, America "matured" in its confidence. Adults just fresh from years of a Great Depression and a World War wanted stability more than anything. Risk taking was not a high priority in those early post war years...security was the password.

By the early '60s, the calm was winding down. Pressing social issues were harder to ignore. Segregation and the resulting integration of America had put a stop to the practice of "separate but equal". Now there was only one rest room and one drinking fountain.

Women were changing as well. Their children were now growing up and becoming more independent. Free time, the benefit of all this technology, was allowing mom to load the washer, dryer, and dishwasher with an ease no generation knew in times before. Things were changing quickly from a society of contentment, to one of unrest.

The children themselves, were very content to remain children longer than ever before. The luxury of one's own bedroom fit for a fairy princess, with dolls the likes of which hadn't been seen since the 1880s, was hard to give up. Being "Daddy's Little Girl" was a title not easily surrendered. Besides, what did Mommy know about what came next? She was busy at the shipyard with a rivet gun, or at the USO and possibly living back at home with her parents while the war raged on. How could the mother of the child of the late '50s and early '60s possibly help a girl prepare for a world that mom, much to her regret, never knew?

None of this social change was ignored by the toy industry. In the early '50s, there were basically two kinds of dolls. Baby dolls, and dolls which represented the child herself. Everything was in the present tense. Television commercials of the day showed mommy changing her real live baby, while a perfectly groomed and starched little girl changed HER baby, in doll form along with mommy.

When the little girl of the family had to think of the present, it was through the eyes of Betsy McCall, Ginny, or Madame Alexander's Wendy. Through these dolls, a child could not fear the first day of school, a trip on the train to grandma's, or baking a cake for the very first time. It can not be said enough that the difference between the child of the boom generation and the child of today, is that the emphasis in the late '50s and early '60s was on the present, while today the focus is on growing up as fast as one can.

The start of playing in the future has often been credited to the BARBIE® doll by Mattel, but in actuality, BARBIE® was merely a knock off of a concept that started in 1955 with the Revlon doll by Ideal.

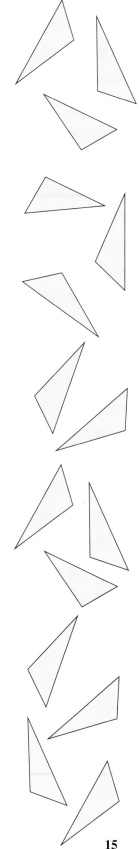

Illustration 10. American Character would take over the Toni home permanent license from Gillette in the late '50s, and use it on a mature full figure doll rather then a child doll that the Ideal Toy Company did in the early '50s. She also would be called *The Toni Doll*.

Illustration 11. The demure Sweet Sue child dolls of the early '50s would become *Sweet Sue Sophisticate* in the late '50s and early '60s. The doll would be advertised as having a real bra and a full figure. Children were now playing in the future instead of the present.

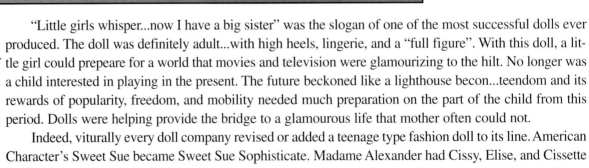

New!
Mary Hoyer's
VICKY DOLL

The newest member of the Mary Hoyer
Doll Family, with complete Wardrobe
from Sportswear to Formals

Illustration 12. Even the Mary Hoyer Doll Company would join in the teenage craze doll race with *Vicky*, who was based on the Revlon dolls of the late '50s and early '60s.

"Little girls whisper...now I have a big sister" was the slogan of one of the most successful dolls ever produced. The doll was definitely adult...with high heels, lingerie, and a "full figure". With this doll, a little girl could prepeare for a world that movies and television were glamourizing to the hilt. No longer was a child interested in playing in the present. The future beckoned like a lighthouse becon...teendom and its rewards of popularity, freedom, and mobility needed much preparation on the part of the child from this period. Dolls were helping provide the bridge to a glamourous life that mother often could not.

Indeed, viturally every doll company revised or added a teenage type fashion doll to its line. American Character's Sweet Sue became Sweet Sue Sophisticate. Madame Alexander had Cissy, Elise, and Cissette with sumptuous adult wardrobes so highly prized today. Vogue dolls gave their famous child doll, Ginny, a big sister Jill and even a friend Jan who was the same size and could share all Jill's wonderful clothing.

Even lesser manufacturers promoted the new "adult figured" dolls in supermarkets, drugstores and outlets from the finest of department stores, to the local hardware outlet. Bride dolls were especially popular as the baby boomer princess dreamed of the day when she could have her own castle over which she would be queen. The cycle was changing, but lots more was still to come!

Illustration 13. Vogue Dolls little toddler girl, Ginny, would acquire a big sister Jill in the late '50s. By the early '60s, *Jill* and her friend Jan would share clothing years before Mattel's BARBIE® and Midge dolls did. Shown also is *Jeff*, a part of the Vogue doll family and the forerunner of Mattel's Ken doll.

Illustration 14. Horsman's *Cindy* was a less expensive version of the popular fashion dolls of the late '50s and early '60s. She was available in three sizes.

Illustration 15. Uneeda would introduce an all jointed teenage fashion doll named *Dolliken* in the late '50s. She was so popular that Ideal manufactured a few rare Revlons with jointed knees in the early '60s.

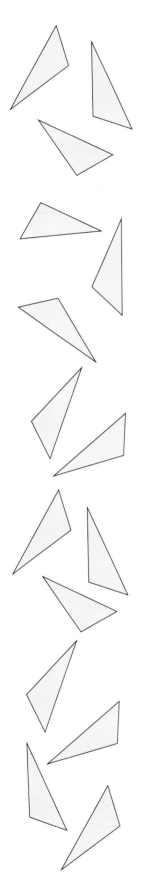

In the mid '50s, Mattel Toys decided that the time was ripe to enter the teenage doll arena. One must understand that Ruth Handler, the driving force behind BARBIE® doll, was not interested in making just another teenage doll. She wanted to make the ultimate teenage fashion doll. To say she succeeded would be an understatement. The BARBIE® doll would forever change play patterns and the way that little girls would view themselves. To some the BARBIE® doll is the best thing that ever happened...to others the doll is a symptom of society at its materialistic worst. No matter what one's personal viewpoints are, the doll is the best selling toy in the history of the world to this very day.

Mattel took the concept of the Revlon doll, Cissy, Sweet Sue Sophisticate, Jill and Jan and their sharing of wardrobes, several steps further. Because so many of BARBIE® doll's exquisite outfits were designed in the mid '50s, they were already dated by the time of the release of the doll in 1959. Modeled after a German doll, Lilli, from a sexy comic strip heroine, BARBIE® doll had features that were not particularly welcomed at first.

After a few quick changes, (four in the course of one year), the final doll with flesh toned skin, blue eyes, and a silky blonde or brunette ponytail was brought before the REAL test market, America's children, via television...the newest technique in marketing.

It mattered little to many little girls (and some boys) if parents objected to the doll...they HAD to have it. Many went to such great lengths to own this tiny piece of perfection, that today it is difficult to expain why, but the obvious answer is that the doll mesmerized an entire generation.

Who can forget sitting in school staring at the fashion booklets included with the basic doll and calculating the strategy to get the money to increase BARBIE® dolls wardrobe? School lunches never bought..dues never paid, all added up quickly. Within two years of its release, the doll had become an American insitution and one that will undoubtedly continue into the future long beyond our time.

With the image of BARBIE® doll firmly entrenched, two interesting phenomena occurred. First, girls and some boys were NOT giving up BARBIE® just because they were deemed "too old" by adults to have the toy. Girls who were dating in the 9th grade would come home and eagerly change BARBIE® doll into her newest and choicest outfit.

Interestingly, there was no social stigma attached to this for many. Girls UNDERSTOOD this phenomenon. The very same young teenagers drooling over Ricky Nelson and Fabian, were also swapping BARBIE® accessories. Many NEVER gave up their obsession with BARBIE® doll, continuing to buy the latest dolls and fashions even to this day.

No matter how you feel about the BARBIE® doll, one thing is certain. This toy alone shaped ALL of the Sensational '60s dolls, for BARBIE® doll was the standard that every toy was judged against. Even the dazzling wardrobes of the Madame Alexander fashion dolls were not enough to compete with lower priced Mattel ensembles of exceptional quality that were sold EVERYWHERE, and not just in the "better" stores.

Manufacturers would ask...if another toy or doll was different, would it capture enough of the market share to warrant the manufacturing of this item? Even the other best selling dolls of the period tried to imitate the fashion doll theme in some other way (such as Ideal's Tammy with a more wholesome figure, or American Character's Tressy with added hair play value). Other dolls and toys tried to disassociate themselves from the BARBIE® doll by focusing on television shows like "The Flintstones", "The Jetsons", or other popular animated cartoon shows that made Saturday morning a boob-tube event. Even so, without any question, it was the BARBIE® doll that changed the way children and young teenagers viewed dolls and toys forever.

The early '60s was in many ways just like the '50s until the BARBIE® doll came along. Children then viewed themselves as just waiting in the wings to be a teenager. Many an eight year old at the time would state that they were temporarily miserable until that magic time when they could be thirteen...and the world of teendom with all its promises would be theirs...the focus had changed once again, and would change several times before the decade was over. The *Sensational '60s* had arrived. Things would never be the same!

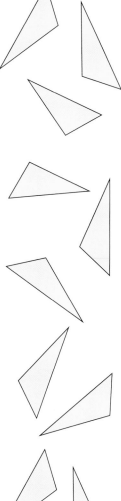

Illustration 16. The doll of the decade, *BARBIE®* by Mattel. This first BARBIE® is very rare in that she has not changed skin tones to a milky white. She does have the arched eyebrows and white irises and holes in her feet which identify her as the number one BARBIE® doll released in March of 1959.

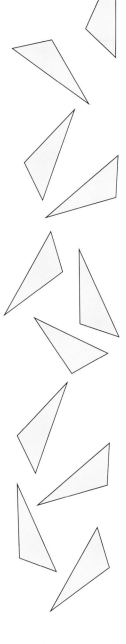

Illustration 17. Shown only in the 1959 catalog are the most desirable of the early BARBIE® doll ensembles. From left is *Easter Parade, Gay Parisienne,* and *Roman Holiday Separates.* All sell today for over $1,000 when complete and in mint condition. Add a couple of thousand if still in the original packaging.

Illustration 18. 1960 *number two BARBIE® doll wearing Gay Parisienne.*

EARLY '60S DOLLS

While the beginning years of the 1960s saw the birth of the BARBIE® doll, the impact would not be felt until around 1962-63. Other manufacturers watched with both a mixture of amazement and horror as they saw the impact that this new style of doll had on the toy industry.

The Madame Alexander doll company had prided itself on top of the line dolls for "the carriage trade." Alexander dolls promoted love of the classics in art, literature and fairy tales. The philosophy behind an Alexander doll was that Madame Alexander and her design team would take a basic doll mannequin, in sizes that ranged from 8 to 36 inches, and create a storybook or literary character with the skillful manipulation of facial painting, hairstyling, and clothing. Often the entire Alexander line for any given year would consist of less than six basic doll mannequins that were turned into a hundred or more distinctive characters by the creative genius of the Alexander Doll Company.

Madame Alexander believed very strongly that a child's exposure to the fine arts was a necessary part of the maturation process. If for some reason that involvement was limited, then a doll representing the arts would be available to help the child assimilate the knowledge of the past centuries. It was called a liberal arts education and many a college student would major in this now almost extinct gentile way of self expression.

Other companies such as Effanbee and American Character still thought that little girls would love to play mommy, and issued lavish baby doll layette sets that were aimed at the traditional girl child who for the moment, thought that the nurturing of her offspring would be fulfilling enough.

The one thing that separated the child of the '50s and those of the '60s was television. The magic box, a luxury in homes a decade before, now in the '60s was almost a universal commodity. As a new medium for entertainment, so it was also for advertising.

Up until now, the choice of a child's toy was up to the parent. This decision was often guided by such well respected establishments as the *Good*

Illustration 19. The face of the *number one BARBIE®* introduced in 1959, with her white irises and arched eyebrows, was judged to be too harsh to be an American girl. Still, the doll, with some revisions would go on to be the best selling toy in the world.

Illustration 21. The back of the *Babs* doll clothing boxes was identical in every way to the clothing boxes of the BARBIE® doll. The free enterprise system was alive and thriving.

Illustration 20. Because BARBIE® doll was so successful, almost overnight came the imitations. Here is *Babs*, a very inexpensive knock-off of the number one BARBIE®. Made by Fab Lu Dolls Company, New York.

Illustration 22. The Fab Lu Babs doll even had a boyfriend that was a direct knock off of Ken called, *Bill*. Even the fashions were identical in color and theme.

Illustration 23. By the 1960s, the third *BARBIE®* doll would still be a bit on the pale side, but would have curved eyebrows and blue irises that would make her look much more American.

Housekeeping Seal of Approval and *Parents Magazine's* Award of Excellence. Little did parents realize that advertisers not happy with their decisions as to the choice of playthings for their offspring would take their products directly to the child. These blitzkrieg assaults would occur each afternoon and again all day Saturday in an all out assault to convince a little boy or girl that their life was somehow askew if they did not own the latest toy craze item that was being promoted.

Even Mattel themselves, not fully confident of BARBIE® dolls appeal, advertised more traditional toys such as Chatty Cathy, Chatty Baby, and games aimed at both boys and girls. Slowly but surely the focus changed from a decision made by the parents, to one made by the child who was almost drugged into believing that their lives would be ruined without these toys that were rammed down their throats hour after hour in front of the electronic baby sitter. This "fill-in" for parents would continue to be an ever increasing presence in the family as mothers were economically forced to work outside the home to make ends meet. At the end of a long day, or a sleep-in Saturday morning, it was often a necessity to plop the children in front of the television. There while the adults slept came the action heroes and adventuresome mice AND the hard sell, hard edge commercial that parents often didn't even see. These advertising monologues were extremely successful in convincing the child that their life was unfulfilled without the best selling dolls of the day.

Often the doll seemed larger than life on the television screen, able to move and so filled with love, that a child lonely from lack of attention felt that with the addition of this doll, their dream of that perfect little friend would become a reality. It was like getting a new puppy, but without all the mess and the clean-ups...the doll was theirs, forever to make them happy. It was still a world everyone could live with. But still, more changes lay ahead after the Camelot years.

Illustration 24. *BARBIE®* and *Ken®*, circa 1961-62. The fourth BARBIE® doll would now have pinker, more natural skin tones, while Ken doll sported a molded crew cut. They were the all American couple and the idols of not only children, but young teenagers as well.

Illustration 25. In 1961, the Bubble Cut hairstyle was introduced on the BARBIE® doll. Many said that she looked like Elizabeth Taylor. It is rare today to find the 1961 *Bubble Cut* with black hair and big red lips.

Illustration 26. The lure of BARBIE® and Ken was always the lifestyle that they led. As teen leaders, naturally they would have a wonderful car such as this *Hot Rod* by Irwin Toys.

Illustration 27. This very rare lemon yellow blonde *BARBIE*® is the fifth style doll issued in 1962, and identified by her firm bangs and smaller lips. While looking very all American, she still had her roots in the '50s.

Illustration 28. A very rare *Matty Mattel* that still talks in the original packaging from the early '60s. The television commercials featured Matty Mattel telling children that "You can tell it's Mattel...it's swell!"

Illustration 29. A very rare *Sister Belle* who along with Matty proclaimed the message that Mattel was the leader of the toy industry in the early '60s.

Illustration 30. What '60s child did not watch Beany and Cecil? Here a Mattel talking *Beany* waits for *Cecil the Seasick Sea Serpent* to come and talk with him.

Illustration 31. A perfect mint in box 1960 *Chatty Cathy* with all the accessories she came with. Dolls like this are increasingly harder to find in this condition and when do, bring about book value. Also in the box was a plastic shoe horn to help Chatty Cathy get into her shoes!

Illustration 32. This rare brunette dog eared *Chatty Cathy* has blue eyes and her original wrist tag. These dolls represented the children of the early '60s at their finest.

Illustration 33. *Chatty Cathy paper dolls* by Whitman allowed the doll to seem real to the child who loved her.

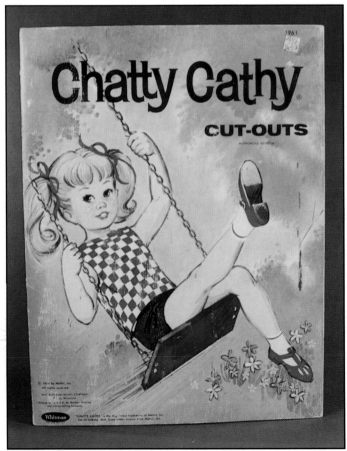

Illustration 34. The back of the Whitman *Chatty Cathy paper doll* showed both real and fictitious outfits for Chatty Cathy.

Illustration 35. A very few rare black *Chatty Cathy* dolls were made and not widely distributed. These dolls are very sought after today by collectors of all races.

Illustration 36. The second type of packaging showed the face of *Chatty Cathy* through a cut-out in the box. Children once trained to never open a box in a toy store without asking, were now eager to see the contents due to the television advertising campaigns of the period.

36

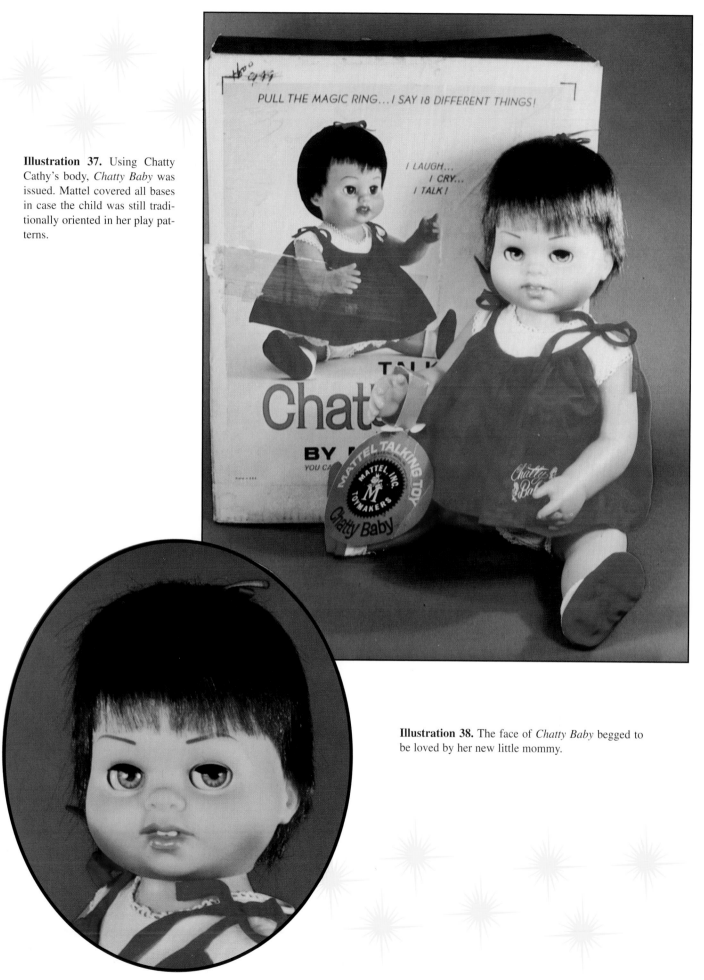

Illustration 37. Using Chatty Cathy's body, *Chatty Baby* was issued. Mattel covered all bases in case the child was still traditionally oriented in her play patterns.

PULL THE MAGIC RING... I SAY 18 DIFFERENT THINGS!

I LAUGH...
I CRY...
I TALK !

TALK
Chat
BY
YOU CA

MATTEL TALKING TOY
MATTEL, INC.
TOYMAKERS
Chatty Baby

Illustration 38. The face of *Chatty Baby* begged to be loved by her new little mommy.

Illustration 40. *Tiny Chatty Brother* added to the desire for a child to have a miniature friend to love. This was an adorable doll seldom found in mint condition today.

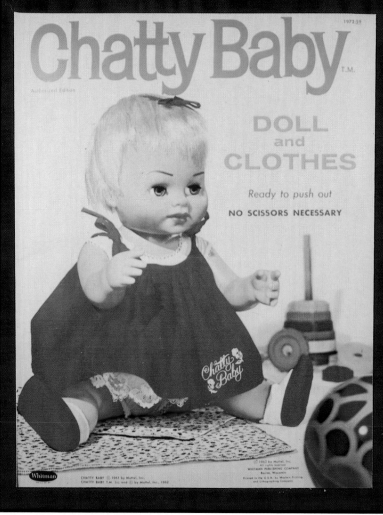

Illustration 39. Naturally Whitman paper dolls were made to represent *Chatty Baby* and add to the realistic play patterns.

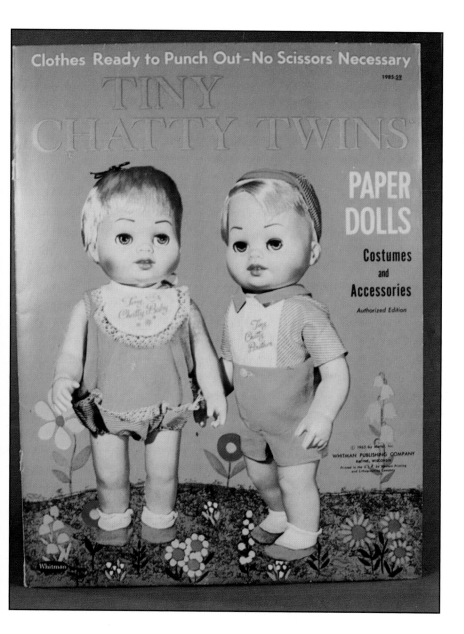

Clothes Ready to Punch Out-No Scissors Necessary

TINY CHATTY TWINS

PAPER DOLLS

Costumes and Accessories

Authorized Edition

WHITMAN PUBLISHING COMPANY

Illustration 41. *Tiny Chatty Baby* was the twin sister to Tiny Chatty Brother, and Whitman again captured them in paper doll form in the early '60s.

Illustration 42. By 1963, this whimsical, wonderful playmate, *Charmin' Chatty*, was added to the talking doll line. She is a favorite of just about any Chatty collector.

Illustration 43. Remco's *The Littlechap Family* was a study of the American Dream. Modeled after a doctor and his former fashion model wife and their two exemplary children, they were paragons of virtue in the Camelot years of the early '60s.

Illustration 44. *Judy Littlechap* by Remco. Many say that she was modeled after Jacqueline Kennedy. Sure looks like it to me!

Illustration 45. Madame Alexander was still making basic dolls to help little girls play in the present. In 1960-61, *Maggie Mix-up* was an 8in all hard plastic doll that allowed a little girl to stay young a bit longer.

Illustration 46. Madame Alexander issued this 21in *Jacqueline*, wearing a copy of Mrs. Kennedy's Inaugural Ball gown. Later the White House would ask that this unofficial doll be taken out of the line. It was a moot point, because due to the assassination of President Kennedy, the 1962 Jacqueline and Caroline, (and even a prototype of John-John) line was rapidly discontinued.

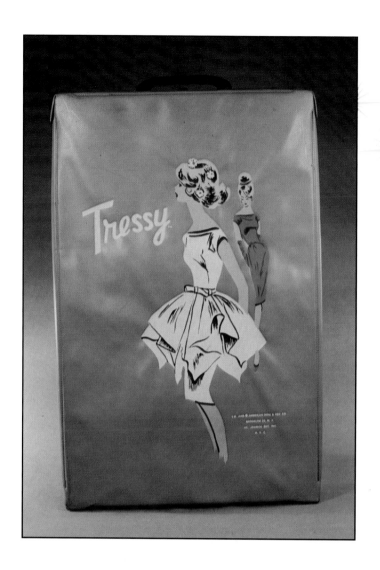

Illustration 47. American Character's *Tressy* was basically a BARBIE® doll knock-off, but had the added value of hair play. This rare case for the doll and her clothes shows the artwork popular in the early '60s.

Illustration 48. Much to the chagrin of BARBIE® doll collectors, *Tressy* outfits are much, much harder to find NRFB. The quality is excellent, but they have not seen much increase in value due to lack of interest. The true Tressy collector, with much difficulty, can amass a collection far rarer than that of BARBIE® doll outfits from the same period.

Illustration 49. A very, very rare black version of *Tressy*. Almost never seen for sale, this doll is the jewel in the crown of a Tressy collector.

Illustration 50. Vince Edwards played *Dr. Ben Casey* on television from 1961 to 1966. This doll of him was manufactured in the early '60s and was an excellent replication of the star.

Illlustration 51. Another doctor of television fame was *Dr. Kildare* as portrayed by Richard Chamberlain. The doll came with an autographed photo of the star of the television show which ran from 1961-1966. Remco Toys was the maker of this admirable likeness.

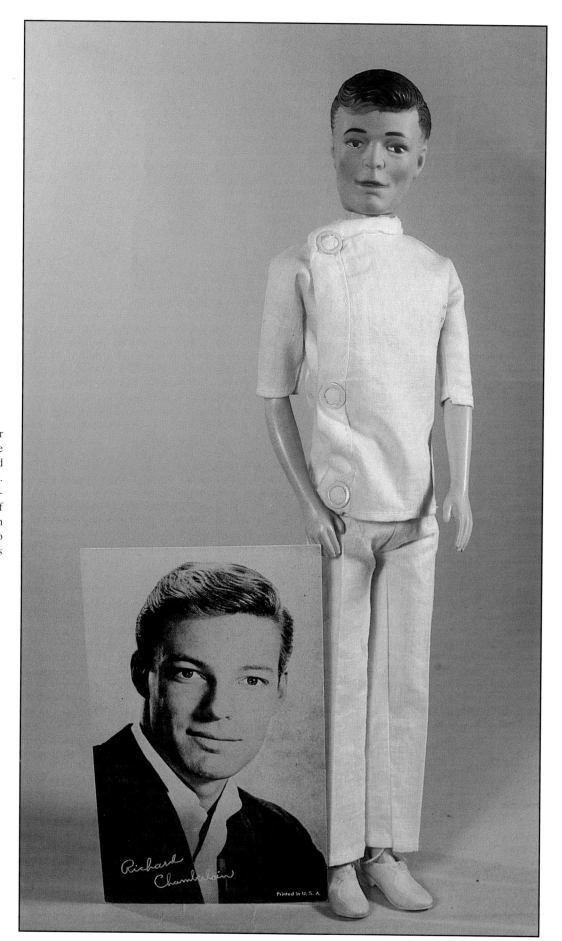

Illustration 52. The BARBIE® doll was firmly entrenched in American pop culture. This *Fashion Queen BARBIE®* from 1963, wears an Egyptian style turban, undoubtedly inspired by the movie *Cleopatra* with Elizabeth Taylor. Note the Mattel store display in the background that showed a beautiful girl and her wonderful life in fantastic artwork.

Illustration 53. In 1962, the Ideal Toy corporation thought that with the *Tammy* doll, loosely based on the Debbie Reynolds movies, they could capture the wholesome side of the fashion doll market. They did, but only for a few years. Tammy is a wonderful doll and highly collectible.

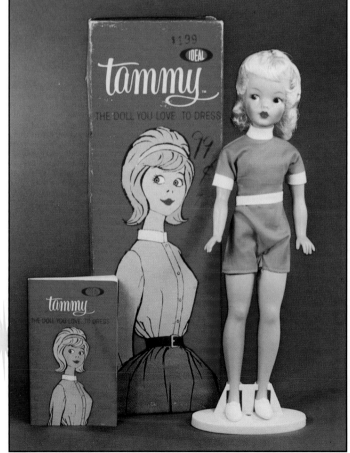

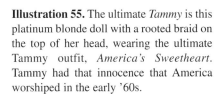

Illustration 54. *Tammy's* life was that of a typical teenager. She was not a top fashion model, nor did she fly to Paris or Rome on assignments. She lived the life most teens did during the early '60s. Hours on the phone, record hops, and clothes were her undying passions.

Illustration 55. The ultimate *Tammy* is this platinum blonde doll with a rooted braid on the top of her head, wearing the ultimate Tammy outfit, *America's Sweetheart*. Tammy had that innocence that America worshiped in the early '60s.

Illustration 56. Madame Alexander tried desperately to capture the fashion doll market as late as 1966. Her *Coco* doll, loosely based on Coco Channel, was dressed in an Yves Saint Laurent inspired dress, which actually is taken from a Mondrian painting decades earlier. This doll was not shown in the Alexander catalogs and is extremely rare.

MID '60s DOLLS

It seemed as if it was the end of the world...the doll world. The BARBIE® doll had gripped the nation in a strangle hold that shook the very foundations of companies that existed decades before an 11-1/2 inch, heavy chested wonder arrived on the scene.

To the Alexander Doll Company, the BARBIE® doll must have been seen as a temporary flash of bad taste. Surely this new phenomenon could not erase decades of success. Yet that was just the case in many instances. The Alexander Doll Company paid a great deal of money to obtain the Brenda Starr name for a teen fashion doll. Despite her wonderful sleep eyes and designer wardrobe, she was not the magical and mystical BARBIE® doll. The next year, the same doll issued under the name Yolanda would fail miserably as well. Alexander would withdraw from the fashion doll race and remain faithful to their 8 inch hard plastic dolls dressed a couple of hundred different ways each year.

The British invasion was the final nail in the coffin of children wanting to remain children. Now even the most conservative family had at least one child who wanted the new mini skirts, or a son who craved striped stove pipe pants. Hair styles became more than just self expression. The way one wore their hair signified if you were part of the "establishment" (those over thirty), or part of the youth cult. It was quite an oxymoron that one had to quickly grow up, but then

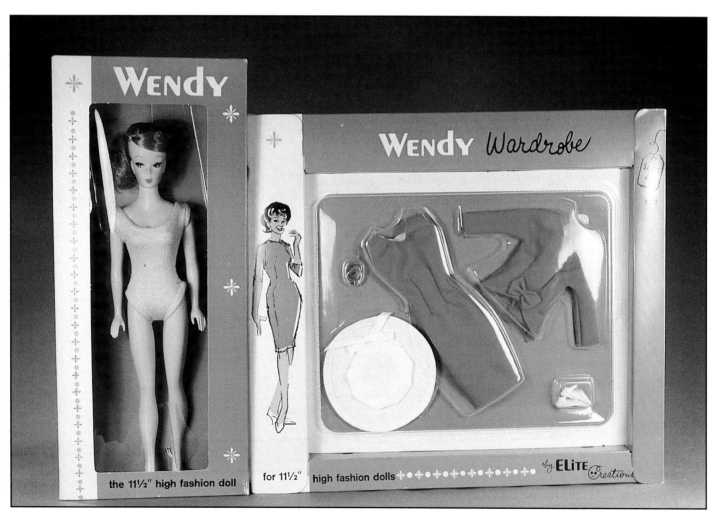

Illustration 57. Knock-offs of the BARBIE® doll continued and still do to this day, but not quite so blatantly today because of stronger laws. This is *Wendy* from the Elite Doll Company. The quality of these dolls was usually very poor and most children could easily tell this was not a BARBIE® doll.

Illustration 58. The Vogue Doll Company introduced the last of the *Ginny* dolls dressed as little girls in the mid
'60s. The first, like the one shown here, had a plastic body with a vinyl head. The later dolls would be all vinyl.
It was the end of an era for "The Fashion Leaders of Doll Society", the Vogue Doll Company trademark.

just as quickly stop before the appointed age of the end of life...thirty years old.

Mattel had thought that BARBIE® would always be secure in her position as a doll that represented the wholesome, yet sexy American teenage girl. BARBIE® was aging. In a daring move she was allowed to grow up and now attended college. The high school themed outfits now gave way to ensembles called "Sorority Meeting" and "Fashion Editor". But, as youth became more and more rebellious against the established ways, would a little girl or boy, want to play with BARBIE® and Ken dolls that still resembled Sandra Dee and Troy Donahue? What DID these kids want anyway? Did they themselves really know?

The younger child of the mid '60s was dropping out of doll play at an ever increasingly earlier age. Interestingly, this was a mixed blessing for the toy industry. Younger children were far less quality conscious than their older counterparts. "Suggestions" of accessories could now pass for the elaborate and detailed older ones. The other side of the picture was that this child, TOTALLY raised in the television era, was not so easy to entertain with a toy. The doll had to DO something to amuse the child. This generation, born after 1964 and often called Generation X, was raised with excitement, adventure, and an eerie knowledge that those that came slightly before them had been called smarter, more clever, and destined to succeed. Many of the new Generation Xers secretly knew that once they left Mom and Dad's economics, the hundred a pop sneakers they took for granted would not be within their financial grasp.

The typical five year old of the mid '60s wanted the toy to create the mood, and then actually do something to make that mood. New technology gave dolls the ability to not only walk with help, but on their own with battery operated mechanisms. Soon dolls that could sit on the potty, recite nursery rhymes at random, and rock their own cradles filled the toy shelves trying to desperately compete with the BARBIE® doll.

Television shows were inspiring hosts of dolls as well. The "Patty Duke Show", "Bewitched" and "I Dream of Jeannie" were the inspiration for dolls of the female leads. Well done, and today quite collectible, they were the answer to having a doll become a decorative accessory in one's room instead of just a play toy.

Little boys were viewed as an untapped market for dolls as well. Research showed that far more little boys than parents would like to admit, owned a Ken doll and even a BARBIE® or two in secret. Hasbro responded to this by making GI Joe®, America's Fighting Hero in 1964. The inspiration was the Ken doll, but with a military theme to make the doll more "masculine". Naturally since most children are fascinated with dolls and love imaginary friends, this doll for boys was a big success. Carefully called an "action figure", it still was a doll with a wardrobe. By the late '60s, however, the direction of even GI Joe® would change from one of a conquering military hero, to an action adventure man who chased tigers and lost temples instead of left over war criminals.

All in all, during this period of tremendous change in American youth, the children of this new generation seemed apathetic to most anything except what was popular on television. The toy industry was taking a deep breath and examining where things were heading...a shake down was coming, and many would rise up better than ever from the fires of the nations discontent. The decade was redefining itself all over again. In the highly competitive toy business, now one had to run as fast as the wind itself, just to keep even. Even more surprising changes lay ahead in the late '60s.

Illustration 60. The fully articulated doll or figure of *Hoss Cartwright*.

Illustration 59. American Character Doll Corporation manufactured dolls of the characters on the television show "Bonanza", which ran from 1959-1973. These mid '60s dolls are highly collectible. The artwork on the boxes is outstanding. This is the packaging for the *Hoss* figure, played by the late Dan Blocker.

Illustration 61. The American Character Doll Company packaging for the *Little Joe Cartwright* doll.

Illustration 62. The actual figure of *Little Joe Cartwright*, played by the late Michael Landon.

Illustration 63. The Ideal Tammy family continued in the mid '60s with the addition of new characters. A hard-to-find doll is this *Dodi* doll, who was Tammy's Little Sister Pepper's friend.

Illustration 64. The back of the Dodi box showed all the fabulous fashions available for *Pepper* and *Dodi*. Notice that the styles illustrated are still very '50s inspired, but that would all change rapidly in the next few years.

Illustration 66. The *Mary Make-Up* box is very rare and shows a mirror with the face of the mid '60s.

Illustration 67. An advertising brochure for *Mary Make-Up* telling of her secrets.

Illustration 65. American Character tried desperately to hold onto a market share of the fashion doll movement by making a new friend for Tressy, *Mary Make-Up.* The doll would concentrate on make-up play as Tressy did on hair styling fun. The fashion booklet is very hard to find and inside are the beginnings of great fashion changes for teenagers.

Do you know Mary Make-Up's Glamour Secrets?

Mary Make-Up is Tressy's best friend. Tressy lends Mary Make-Up her special glamour kits so you can change her make-up and hair color to match her moods and her clothes. With these exclusive kits, you can make Mary pretty so many different ways.

Mary Make-Up uses Tressy's cosmetic kit, containing blushing lipstick, fine-line eyebrow pencil, eye shadow, cosmetic sponges, nail polish and perfume too —just like a glamourous model's.

Mary Make-Up uses Tressy's hair coloring kit, containing 3 glamourous hair colors —Golden Blonde, Red and Brunette—in easy to use applicators.

Both the cosmetics and hair colors are safe to use and wash off easily, so you can change Mary's make-up and hair color over and over again.

Now—in Mary Make-Up's Special Offer—Get Both Tressy's Cosmetic Kit and Hair Coloring Kit for only $3.00.

USE THIS CONVENIENT COUPON TO ORDER YOUR GLAMOUR KITS NOW!

Mail To:
DOLL COSMETICS
Box No. 854
Brooklyn, N.Y. 11202

I enclose check or money order for $3.00 which includes postage and handling. Please send me both the COSMETIC KIT and HAIR COLORING KIT.

Name _____ Child's Age _____

Street _____

City _____ State _____ Zip Code _____

Offer good only in Continental U.S. Allow 3 weeks for delivery. This offer expires January 1, 1967.

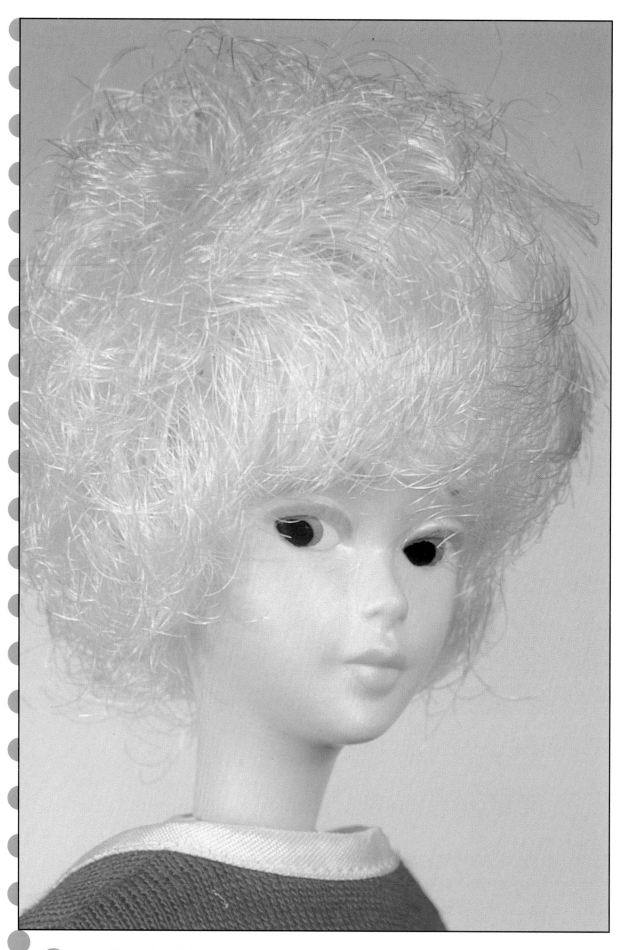

Illustration 68. The unmade-up face of *Mary Make-up* also showed the new short teased hair that would come into vogue and them quickly disappear.

Illustration 69. *Glamour Misty* dressed in the outfit shown in *Illustration 70.* The beginning of the British rock star invasion can be seen in this Carnaby Street inspired fashion.

Illustration 70. Tammy doll by Ideal also acquired a new friend in the mid '60s called *Glamour Misty*. Featuring a beautifully sculpted body and fantastic hair, her clothing was crossing the line into MOD! She was a very exciting doll from this period.

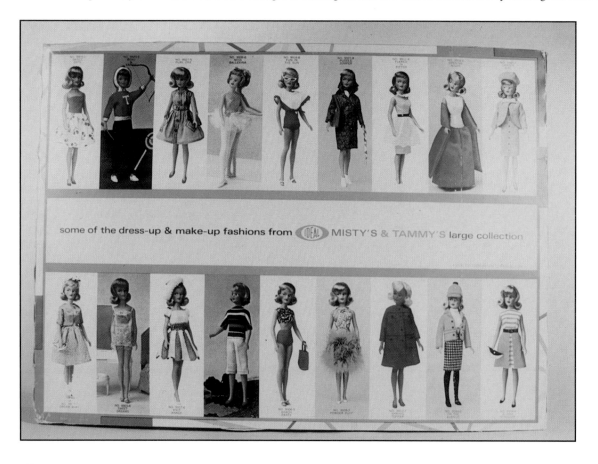

some of the dress-up & make-up fashions from ⬭IDEAL MISTY'S & TAMMY'S large collection

Illustration 71. The back of the clothing boxes showed the very rare fashions for *Tammy* and *Glamour Misty*. The author has only located four of these fashions in never removed from box condition in fifteen years! They are far rarer than any BARBIE® doll fashion.

Illustration 72. *Glamour Misty* is ready to meet the Beatles in this sweatshirt that was a pak accessory for Tammy and Glamour Misty. The Beatles are not named on the shirt, but there is no question it is them. "Ya Ya Ya" was a lyric from their song, "She Loves You".

Illustration 73. Another popular television show was "The Flintstones". *Baby Bam Bam* was captured by Ideal in doll form straight from Bedrock, hometown of the Flintstones and their neighbors, the Rubbles.

Illustration 74. The *Bam Bam* doll by Ideal. He was available in a smaller size as well.

Illustration 75. Available in 1964 for a couple of years, was *Penny Brite* by Deluxe Reading. In my opinion, this doll is the last of the great child dolls of moderate price and high quality. The doll came in a plastic box that could also serve as an armoire. This was an idea that Ideal and Mattel would both utilize in the future.

Illustration 76. The back of the *Penny Brite* fashion boxes showed the image of a little girl jumping rope. Because times were changing so quickly, some of the outfits themselves would depict typical teenage activities such as talking on the telephone.

Illustrations 77-82. The six different ensembles available for *Penny Brite*. Also available was a school room, a kitchen, a beauty salon and a bedroom. Each came with an extra outfit on a cardboard figure that was only sold with the accessory set.

Illustration 77.

Illustration 78.

Illustration 79.

Illustration 80.

Illustration 81.

Illustration 82.

Illustration 83. Even old favorites were still around like this Uneeda Doll Company version of *Betsy McCall*. Endorsed in women's magazines by actress Carol Channing, the doll just could not compete with BARBIE® doll. Collectors today appreciate dolls like this as a piece of American history.

Illustration 84. Remco was another company that tried desperately to capture a piece of the little girl playing in the present idea that was a rapidly fading market in the mid '60s. Their *Heidi* doll was of wonderful quality, much like the Vogue Ginny doll of the '50s.

Illustration 85. Remco's *Heidi* came in a plastic box that could hold clothing. Naturally the quality level reflected the fact that the Golden Age of dolls was over and would be for the next twenty-five years.

Illustration 86. In a really daring move for the period, Heidi had a best friend *Jan* who was Oriental. This was the BARBIE®/Midge concept, but with an interesting twist. Jan is beautifully sculpted and is very under-evaluated today, in my opinion.

Illustration 87. Remco's *Jan* with her delicate face and plastic case, was a perfect companion to Heidi.

Illustration 88. Inexpensive clothing ensembles were available for *Heidi* and *Jan*. This outfit consisted of three ensembles complete with tiny shoes.

Illustration 89. A deluxe accessory for Jan featured an oriental table and kimono. This is a very difficult fashion to locate today.

Illustration 90. Smarty, a popular doll by the Alexander doll company, was issued in a black version and called *Katie* in 1965. Minorities were becoming more socio-econically connected, and thus wanted better quality dolls that reflected their higher income levels.

Illustration 91. The face mold used on the Coco dolls was also used on the 1966 Portrait dolls from the Alexander Doll Company. This is the *Scarlett* doll, and is considered to be one of the rarest of the six Portrait dolls of that year.

Illustration 92. *Barbie Goes to College*! Mattel, in a daring move, allowed BARBIE® to grow up in a Sears exclusive set, *Barbie Goes to College*. All the outfit names for the next two years, would reflect that BARBIE® doll had graduated from High school and now had moved on. Critics of the BARBIE® doll are not often aware of the motivation that the doll gave to little girls of the period to be the first generation of the family to attend college.

Illustration 93. The life of BARBIE® and her little sister Skipper is portrayed in this notebook from Standard Plastics Products in 1964. The value of this rare item is about $600! The piece of the American Dream that the BARBIE® doll represents is a valuable commodity to today's collectors.

Illustration 94. By 1965, the world of BARBIE® had expanded rapidly. With an ever enlarging circle of friends who could all "share" the same size clothing, BARBIE® doll's popularity had gone far beyond her 1959 expectations. This fashion booklet alone is very hard to find today in mint condition.

Illustration 95. A *1964 Platinum Swirl BARBIE®* doll with pink lips frosted over in white lip gloss (how can we ever forget these fads!), models *Campus Sweetheart*, a very rare BARBIE® outfit from the mid '60s. The bouquet and the trophy are most of the value.

Illustration 96. A close-up of the face of the American teenager, as interpreted through the BARBIE® doll, circa 1965.

Illustration 97. Many oddities exist from the BARBIE® dolls of the period as parts were used up. Here a Swirl head is on a Bendable Leg body with a wide sticker on the box proclaiming that the legs bend.

Illustration 98. The *American Girl Swirl Ponytail* face seen close up. The box is stamped Titian Ponytail so there can be no doubt that this doll is factory original.

Illustration 99. Another very rare BARBIE® is this *American Girl faced Swirl Ponytail BARBIE®* in the original box.

Illustration 100. The BARBIE® persona was continually updated as in this rare record album. One of six records, the voice of BARBIE® told of glamourous teenage situations and the fun that would be yours when you "grew up". The only problem was that the words "grown up" would come to mean "teenager" to an entire generation.

Illustration 101. In 1966, the *Bendable Leg BARBIE®* would have more intense make-up and silky hair. These dolls, issued for one year only, are considered to be the most popular BARBIE® dolls other than a number one, with collectors.

Illustration 102. The early '60s influence is still apparent in these two outfits modeled by very rare dolls. On the left is *Reception Line* and right is *Fashion Luncheon*.

Illustration 103. The rarest of the rare are the *American Girl BARBIE®* dolls with side parted longer hair. They were not featured in any catalog, but were used in Mattel advertising in magazines such as *Jack and Jill.* The outfits are left, *Fraternity Dance* and on the right, *Debutante Ball.* The outfit names tell of a beautiful girl and her wonderful life.

Illustration 104. Also available as a store exclusive is this Sears Mink. Made of the finest ranch mink, it is fully lined in satin and has the BARBIE® label. It sold for about $10.00 in 1966-67 and today is worth close to $2,000!

Illustration 105. Another of the very rare BARBIE® outfits is this *Pan American Airlines Stewardess* outfit. The doll is a very hard to find ash blonde American Girl with intense make-up.

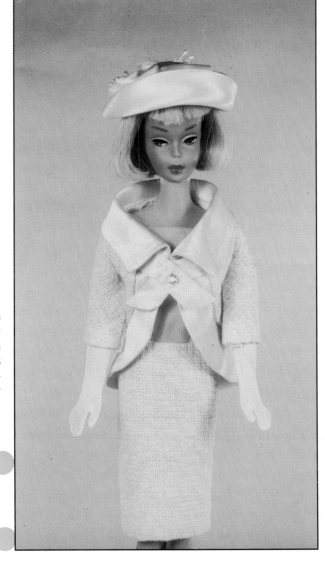

Illustration 106. The outfit *Fashion Luncheon* was the last of the Camelot inspired ensembles. Today it is very popular with collectors and is worth about $1,500 in never removed from box condition. The dolls and outfits from the mid '60s are actually harder to find in mint condition than the earlier dolls because of children's play patterns.

Illustration 107. The *Color Magic* dolls from 1966 are very hard to find in this rare brunette hair color. She is wearing the Sears exclusive *Hostess Set* outfit. The garments were so well made that if enlarged, would be perfectly tailored for a real person! The mid '60s would soon be over as the MOD movement arrived in full swing!

Illustration 108. *Left:* BARBIE® doll's friend *Midge* got a new hairstyle and bendable legs in 1965. She models *International Fair*. *Right:* A gorgeous *Bendable Leg BARBIE®* from 1966 proudly wears *Matinee Fashion*. The days of dressing like this to go to the movies on a Saturday afternoon were sadly drawing to a close. In 1967, the BARBIE® doll would be completely overhauled to keep pace with current fashion, make-up, and hairstyling trends.

Illustration 109. In 1967, Mattel issued BARBIE® doll's cousin *Francie* in a black version. The doll did not sell well, as even blacks could not believe that BARBIE® doll had a black cousin with basically white features sequestered away! Today, however, the doll is one of the most desirable dolls ever produced by Mattel.

Sensational '60s Dolls

PART

II

CHAPTER 4

LATE '60S DOLLS

Perhaps the one factor which forever changed the direction the '60s was moving in was the Vietnam War. The conflict, rapidly escalating into a foreign war offshore, was also being fought domestically here at home, as political feelings ran the gamut from those whose philosophy was "It's my country right or wrong" to "Hell no, we won't go." It would set the tone of the nations youth until the mid '70s and really make the decade last far beyond the stroke of midnight, 1969.

The Baby Boomers, use to a land of milk and honey, were simply emotionally unequipped to deal with the rigors of war in a country they had never heard of. Drug use became rampant to ward off the effects of stress. At home, those same drugs soothed the ravages of families torn apart as one son went to Canada and another off to an undeclared war.

Naturally the children of the time felt this tension all around them. A duality existed as never before. As fashions became more and more radical, those lucky enough to have a valued 2-s Student Deferment from the draft board realized that their rebellion could only be cosmetic, or they would be pulled from the ivory towers quicker than Rapunzel, and sent off to fight in a war that most college students of the period knew very little about.

The BARBIE® doll presented quite a dilemma in the late '60s. Even the presence of BARBIE® doll's boyfriend Ken was a potential powder keg. What side of the conflict was he on? Would BARBIE® really represent the youth of today, or just be a psychedelic mannequin of current radical dressing?

These were important questions as a McCarthist type of witch hunt ensued to make sure that no celebrity was neutral on the subject of Viet Nam. Colleges, my own included, hired professional draft counselors whose job it was to keep you out of the conflict and your tuition dollars and you in school. For those not fortunate enough to be ensconced in higher education, difficult decisions had to be made.

Mattel, ever mindful of the public image of BARBIE® doll and her world, simply discontinued Ken for a year and a half. With him gone from the line, there would be no questions asked as to his political stance.

BARBIE® doll herself would continue to push the limits of good taste in fashions that were ever shorter and bordered on the drug culture with fabric patterns that allegedly were the enhanced images seen while high on LSD, a popular hallucinogenic drug of the time. Giant paisley prints, and outlined letters and flowers dominated outfits accessorized with suede fringe and boots. Still somewhat tastefully done, the outfits increasingly cast a "hippie" rather than just "hip" image on America's favorite doll.

Other dolls with "hip" wardrobes appeared not so much to compete with BARBIE® doll, but to just coexist and grab a small piece of the pie. Today that is rarely done, as often one can't compete with BARBIE® doll and remain financially solvent, in my opinion.

A return to basics by other manufacturers was a desperate attempt to woo the parent who wanted their child to grow up in very traditional ways. The ghettos of hippie lands like Haight Ashbury were a scary thought to the mother of a teenage girl chomping at the bit to be set free. Companies like Alexander and Effanbee, tried and with some measure of success, to stick to dolls that looked like they were made twenty years before. Indeed, many of the Alexander dolls line had NOT changed in twenty years, as the company tried to hold on through another "vulgar" period in America.

The problem was that pop culture and not TRUE culture had become the defining thing of the Generation X children. The life of Ann Marie played by Marlo Thomas on "That Girl" was so much more exciting than the life of Madame Curie. The youth of today LOVED being alive, and while some cavorted too close to the edge with drugs and other horrors, many were content to LOOK like they were groovy, fab, and MOD, if only for appearance sake on the weekend.

The decade would end with basically two kinds of dolls ruling. The fashion doll, as best exemplified

by BARBIE® doll, and classic dolls, as expressed by the Alexander Doll Company, would define the toy industry. Throw in some television toys, a few mechanical dolls, some stuffed animals of favorite Disney characters, and you have the late '60s toy picture. The golden age of beautiful dolls for freshly scrubbed and coiffed little girls was over.

The decade did leave us with many notable dolls as shown here. The 1960s will be remembered as the last decade of quality in dolls until the late 1980s and early 1990s. It was still a wonderful time for a child to enjoy dolls and toys, if only for a brief time until they yearned to move on to a very uncertain, yet always exciting future.

Previous Page: **Illustration 110.** 1964 Disney movie *Mary Poppins*, inspired a host of dolls that lasted into the latter '60s. This 36in "companion doll" of *Mary Poppins* was really the last of the genre of Patti Playpal type of dolls. Things were changing rapidly in the toy industry.

Illustration 111. This 8in *Easter Doll* by the Alexander Doll Company was one of the contemporary beginnings of the "store specials", created just for a particular store in limited quantity in the late '60s. While made in an edition of about 300-320 pieces, sales slips included with the dolls today indicate that back stock was available as late as 1974. Much of this was due to the fact that the doll was not advertised as a store special, and that collectors were not as savvy as they are today.

Illustration 112.
Daisy, by Mary Qwant. This doll, while not a commercial success, was designed by the creator of the mini-skirt. No other fashion defined the '60s as well. The doll was available in England in the mid '60s, and then here for several years after she had been discontinued. A complete wardrobe was available. The illustrations on the packaging were often more interesting than the product.

Illustration 113. The 1967 movie *Dr. Dolittle*, produced many Mattel made collectibles. Here is the *Push-me, Pull-You* complete with Dr. Dolittle. These dolls are some of Mattel's finest creations.

Illustration 114. "The Flying Nun" television series starring Sally Field, was aired from 1967 to 1970. Hasbro introduced this little 4in version of the doll. Like the show, dolls depicting Sister Bertrille were a hit!

Illustration 115. The back of the box of the small size doll featured an actual Screen Gems publicity photograph.

Illustration 116. A deluxe version of *"The Flying Nun"* doll was also available. Fashion doll size, the doll was a big seller for Hasbro. The doll resembled Horsman doll molds.

Illustration 117. Mattel had a hit in two sizes with their *Buffy* from the hit television show "Family Affair". This version talks with Anissa Jones's real voice. It is very popular with collectors today, although the talking mechanism often needs repair which requires opening the box. In my opinion, the doll should be repaired, then just re-shrink wrap the outer box!

Illustration 118. The Alexander Doll Company was still trading off the classics in the late '60s. A series of about twenty-one dolls, called "Portrettes", were issued beginning in 1968 and continued through 1973. This is *Agatha,* who is stunning in red velvet. She dates from 1968.

Illustration 119. This Ideal version of Samantha Stevens, (Elizabeth Montgomery) from the television show "Bewitched", was available in the mid '60s and into the late '60s via mail order catalogs. The role was a strong moment in the women's rights movement, although the brilliance of the storyline would not be recognized until almost present day.

Previous Page: **Illustration 120.** The news for 1967 was that BARBIE® had a new look! Teenage hairstyles and make-up had changed drastically since 1959. The new BARBIE® doll had a more youthful face and long, straight hair. Mattel was so eager to erase the past that they offered the new doll for $1.50 plus your old doll in trade. Millions of dolls were turned in...many were just simply discarded by the retailer, adding to the scarcity of mid '60s dolls.

Illustration 121.
BARBIE® doll's cousin *Francie*™ was introduced in 1966. She was the connection to the ever growing youth cult. Mattel tried to keep BARBIE® doll out of the frenzy by having Francie represent the youth of today. If something went wrong, the company could discontinue Francie, and BARBIE® doll would remain intact. In fact, that is exactly what happened!

Illustration 122. The new face of BAR-BIE® doll was also available in a less expensive version without eyelashes that today, is ironically worth more than the standard doll, as most children wanted the doll with the rooted eyelashes. This generation of children was raised on televi-sion advertising, and knew exactly what they wanted!

Illustration 123. Sears and Roebucks offered many exclusive outfits for BARBIE® doll in the late '60s. This outfit is called *Red Fantastic* and is very hard to locate today without fading. Many collectors, myself included, were unaware that discount stores not in our area, and whose families did not shop their catalogs, had these exclusives at the time that they were offered.

Illustration 124. MOD was a euphemism for modern and as seen here, the BARBIE® doll family was light years away from the image of the early '60s. Shown against vintage wallpaper from the author's bedroom are *Black Franice*, Francie's friend *Casey, Twiggy the Mod model* and a brunette *Francie* doll. It would be a period no one would forget.

Illustration 125. Incredibly MOD gift sets were issued, including this *Barbie Loves the Improvers* gift set from the late '60s. Offered as a mail-in premium from the Inland Steel Company, it is the rarest gift set from the MOD period of the late '60s. Note the almost scandalous outfit constructed of cardboard to resemble a tin can. It was the period of anything goes.

Illustration 126. The Barbie Fan Club offered an outfit called *Salute to Silver*. Featuring a silver lamé mini skirt, it was a smash hit. The doll is a high color *Talkin' BARBIE*® with rare light blonde hair.

Illustration 127. While hair play was a big feature on dolls, the popular hairstyles of the period were often created by such hair artists as Vidal Sassoon. The cut was short, but one length with bangs and very sleek and polished. This "Hair Fair" head, sold separately with wigs, emphasized the fact that MOD could take many different forms. Ironically, this hairstyle would become a staple of the "newscaster" woman of the 1990s.

Illustration 128. Sears was always at the forefront of Barbie fashions. Here, two regular line fashions in different colors were available only in a gift set with dolls from Sears in the late '60s. Note the Nehru collar on Ken and the earings on BARBIE®. Fashion statements like this make for a great doll collection.

Illustration 129. Sears and Roebuck continued to make exclusive outfits for BARBIE® in the late '60s. This outfit is *Glimmer Glamour* and is rarely seen today. When mint, it sells even out of the package for over $1,000.

Illustration 130. *Twist N' Turn Christie* was BARBIE® doll's best friend in the late '60s. Mattel was always in the forefront of the civil rights issues.

Illustration 131. The face of the late '60s would be a fresh and glowing BARBIE® doll with a Marlo Thomas flip hairstyle. Today this is a very popular doll with collectors, especially when mint as the example shown here.

Illustration 132. Already the attitude of the '70s peace movement outfits could be seen here in this 1971 outfit called *Fringe Benefits*. BARBIE® outfits always, even to this day, mirrored current trends and fads.

Illustration 133. BARBIE® doll's friend *P.J.* and her other friend *Walking Jaime*, (a Sears exclusive) were always there to assist BARBIE® doll on her latest adventures, fashionably dressed, of course. PJ models *Check the Suit*, and Walking Jaime is wearing her original mini-skirt outfit that she came in.

Illustration 134. The '60s really belonged to the BARBIE® doll and her groovy friends. The paper dolls would become more and more MOD, and less demure and wholesome as the decade came to a close and a new era, the '70s, began!

Epilogue

Ever wonder today why something looks vaguely familiar? Is it déjà vu? Or are we Baby Boomers just getting older?

The truth is that the '60s and '70s are BACK! When I am on a train or a bus, I watch the youth of today, often I am reminded of myself when I see the way they are dressed. Seldom though am I reminded of myself or my friends when I see how many behave, especially toward adults. Times have changed a great deal in so many ways.

Regardless, in this uncertain economic time, fashion designers feel that if a certain style was a hit once, it can be again with another generation. They must be correct for the endless parade of platform shoes, bell bottoms, long straight hair, and mini skirts keep the memory of the '60s alive.

Supermodels today resemble '60s supermodel Jean Shrimpton, remind me that my generation set fashion trends still popular today.

In dolls, well there is a quality today in some dolls not seen since the '60s, but often beneath that technological wonder is a superficial quality dictated by today's uncertain world of a job today and downsized and out tomorrow.

In my opinion, the terrible uncertainty we live with today contributes to a longing for the '60s. While no on can deny that the world was in a never ending state of change, we all moved along with it as part of it, instead of standing by helpless as is often the case today. This is the lure of the '60s. It simply was and still is the most exciting decade ever in the past several centuries. It was the best time to be young and alive...It truly was the *Sensational '60s*.

Price Guide

Note: The prices given are for the dolls and outfits shown in this book. The pricing of collectibles is a very demanding science! If your item appears to be in better condition than the illustrations, then add to the suggested values. Most Items found today, however, are played with, laundered, or otherwise altered. These articles would naturally bring a much, much lower price. Allow the most for anything still in mint condition, or in the original packaging. Prices vary widely from coast to coast, and theses values should be used only as a guide.

The values given within this book are intended as value guides rather than arbitrarily set prices. The values quoted are as accurate as possible but in the case of errors, typographical, clerical or otherwise, the author and publisher assume no liability nor responsibility for any loss incurred by users of this book.

BIBLIOGRAPHY

Byran, Sandra. *Barbie, The Eyelash Era Fashions 1967-1972*. Sandra Bryan, PO Box 690041, Houston, TX. 1989.

Eames, Sarah Sink. *Barbie Fashion. Vol 1, 1959-1967*. Collectors Books, Paducah, KY. 1990.

Halliwell, Leslie. *Halliwell's Film Guide, 5th edition*. Charles Scribner's Sons, NY. 1985.

McNeil, Alex. *Total Television*. Penguin Books, NY. 1984.

Mandeville, A. Glenn. *Alexander Dolls Collector's Price Guide, 2nd edition*. Hobby House Press, Grantsville, MD. 1995

Mandeville, A. Glenn. *Doll Fashion Anthology and Price Guide, 4th revised Edition*. Hobby House Press, Grantsville, MD. 1993

Mandeville, A. Glenn. *The Golden Age of Collectible Dolls*. Hobby House Press, Grantsville, MD. 1989.

ABOUT THE AUTHOR

A. Glenn Mandeville is regarded among doll collectors as an expert in identifying and appraising modern collectible dolls. He is regularly consulted by thousands of collectors internationally, thus having created a full-time business from his life long hobby of collecting modern dolls. He often lectures and presents slide programs on collectible and modern dolls, and has evaluated more than $3 million worth of collector dolls.

Well-known as a dealer and appraiser of dolls and toys, Mandeville owns an extensive collection that includes Mattel's BARBIE® dolls, Madame Alexander and celebrity dolls, as well as composition dolls, hard plastic dolls from the 1950s, and contemporary doll artist creations.

Mandeville is the author of the acclaimed *Doll Fashion Anthology* book series featuring teen fashion dolls from Tammy, Tressy and Judy Littlechap through BARBIE® dolls. This encyclopedic tome celebrated its 5th edition in 1996. In 1995, he authored the *Alexander Dolls Collector's Price Guide, 2nd Edition*, the definitive work on evaluating Alexander Doll Company, Inc., dolls.

Earlier works include, *Ginny...An American Toddler Doll*, a price guide to Kathe Kruse dolls, *The Celebrity Doll Price Guide and Annual* in 1984 which was co-authored with John Axe, *The Golden Age of Collectible Dolls*, and *Contemporary Doll Stars*, all published by Hobby House Press, Inc.

Mr. Mandeville is founding president of the Delaware Valley Doll Club and a member of the Delaware Valley BARBIE® Club which hosted the 1996 BARBIE® and the Bandstand National BARBIE doll convention, BARBIE O.N.E. and Orange Blossom BARBIE® Club. He has served as Regional Director and chairman of Judges, Modern, for U.F.D.C., Inc. The author is a past presi-

dent of the Madame Alexander Doll Club, and has served on their Board of Directors.

Mandeville's expertise is reflected in his regular television, newspaper, and magazine reports on collectible and modern dolls. His column, "For the Curious Collector" is a regular feature in *Doll Reader®* magazine. He is also a staff writer and pricing editor for *BARBIE® Bazaar* magazine.

Currently residing in the Philadelphia area, Mandeville is presently working on more in depth writing projects.